ICE WORKS CONSTRUCTION GUIDE

Control of groundwater

D. W. Quinion
G. R. Quinion

Thomas Telford
London, 1987

CONTENTS

Published by Thomas Telford Ltd, Telford House, PO Box 101, 26–34 Old Street, London EC1P 1JH

First published 1987

British Library Cataloguing in Publication Data
Quinion, D.W.
 Control of Groundwater. – (ICE works
 construction guides)
 1. Water, Underground 2. Engineering
 geology
 I. Title II. Quinion, G.R. III. Series
 627'.17 TC176

ISBN 0-7277-0362-5

Learning Resources
Centre

Typeset in Great Britain by MHL Typesetting Limited, Coventry
Printed and bound in Great Britain by Henry Ling Limited, at the Dorset Press, Dorchester, Dorset

1. INTRODUCTION

Water power is one of the great forces of nature. Even small quantities of water under high pressure can be destructive: high pressure water jets and low pressure cavitation jets can both be used for cutting materials such as concrete. Water in the ground does not usually attain such significant pressures but in the case of deep mines such as the gold mines in South Africa, the speed and quantity of water entering them limits the depth to which the mine can be worked.

Groundwater originates from the precipitation of rain, sleet or snow and its percolation through the ground. It also arrives by lateral migration of water from water courses, such as rivers, and from the sea. It can enter shallow soils as an upward flow of water, as from springs under artesian pressure, and can also be provided by the discharge of water from treatment plants, the discharges from drainage systems or losses from water mains.

When water enters a soil and is unable to drain away at the same rate the soil is gradually saturated. It may develop a free water table representing the net retention of groundwater. The soil above this level will be partially saturated. In a borehole water might be encountered between layers of impermeable soil; this is known as a confined aquifer condition. Removal of these boundary restraints will usually change the apparent groundwater table level.

The rate at which water flows through the ground will depend on the permeability of the various layers and pockets of soil it encounters and the difference in water table levels between any two places under consideration. It will pass freely through coarse-grained gravels but only slowly through soils of smaller grain sizes than sand. Where an impermeable layer is dished on the top surface or extends for a long distance, there is likely to be a perched water table where the water is held in suspension by the impermeable strata.

Groundwater can be expected to carry chemicals, organic or inorganic, which pass into solution on contact, and as a result be acidic, alkaline or biologically contaminated. The passage of groundwater may dissolve some chemical deposits to create voids which can result in increased permeability or local collapse of the soils.

Surrounding groundwater will flow into excavations below the water table. It is usually necessary to provide dry working conditions in excavations to avoid damage to prepared formations and to work such as reinforced concrete carried out within them. The provision of pumps, pipework and pump attendants to remove and control groundwater can be expensive. The rate at which water may be expected to flow into an excavation after the flow has reached a general state of equilibrium may not be the same as it was initially. Initial pumping usually deals with a reservoir of water in and adjacent to the excavation and once this has been removed it is the continuing inflow which has to be pumped away. Because this depends on the permeabilities of the soils passing the water, the quantity usually drops, although it might rise if pumping were allowed to wash out fine materials from coarser layers and increase their permeability.

In an open excavation, the groundwater, unless intercepted by a surrounding dewatering system or grout curtain, will emerge through the sides of the excavation and run down them until it reaches the water level which is controlled by sump pumping. If these flows of water are not collected in drains or lined trenches and led to the sump or sumps, they will probably erode the sides of the excavation and cause problems. The integrity of the permanent works and the safety of people working in or near the excavation could be placed at risk as a consequence.

In deep excavations, and/or in very permeable soils, measures are usually taken to control groundwater movements. Coffer-dams of steel sheet piling, diaphragm walls, continuous pile walls and similar methods can provide excavations which are little larger than the plan areas of the permanent works they are to contain and preclude significant disruption of adjacent soils and the movement of groundwater through them. Consideration must be given to any high water pressures which may exist in permeable strata below coffer-dams.

The development of cities and urban areas has often caused considerable lowering of the previous groundwater levels due to individuals pumping from their own wells and boreholes. The change-over to piped water supplies in recent decades has enabled the water tables to recover toward much higher levels, but existing water level information under conurbations should always be checked before use. The Water Resources Board and the British Geological Survey regularly publish records of water table levels in many parts of the UK. The conse-quences of such rises in water tables are that many basements and tunnels are now subject to external water pressures which had not previously been anticipated.

The designer of permanent foundations and services needs to anticipate and assess the effects of likely groundwater changes on these works. The contractor will need to anticipate the costs and risk implications and to predict the groundwater conditions and their influence on the entry of groundwater into his excavation. He will need to know how rainfall or water migrating from nearby water courses will affect the soils in, or on, which he is working. He must assess how to maintain good operating conditions for workmen, plant and transport and how to avoid deterioration of acceptable formations and fill materials. Some soils, such as certain chalks, can be quickly saturated by heavy rainfall and their properties impaired, but if left to drain for a short time work can often be resumed without the rain having had an adverse effect.

This guide outlines the information required to select not only a suitable groundwater control system but also a construction method for the work to be constructed below ground level. It complements practical control of groundwater on site,[1] a report published by the Construction Industry Research and Information Association (CIRIA), which provides a detailed exposition of groundwater control, how to design using the many available systems, and detailed advice on equipments and applications. Other CIRIA publications concern construction below ground. Technical Note 95 describes the use of proprietary trench support systems and Technical Report 97 gives guidance on trenching practice.

2. THE INVESTIGATION OF SOIL AND GROUNDWATER CONDITIONS

Site investigations

For the design of foundations, services and other works constructed below ground level, the relevant properties of the ground need to be assessed. It is also necessary to assess whether the existing soil properties and groundwater regime on and adjacent to the site are likely to be significantly altered as a consequence of development on the site and the implications of any such alterations. Depending on the type of work, the nature of the soils and existing knowledge, a site investigation may be undertaken. The decision as to whether or not this is necessary should be taken by the engineer, who should consider the need for measured assessments of ground strata, levels and composition, safe soil bearing capacities, settlement characteristics, soil permeabilities, chemical contaminants and groundwater conditions. Table 1 identifies ground conditions as shown by soil samples.

Site investigations are a composition of qualitative observation and quantitative in situ and laboratory tests coupled with observations of geology, geomorphology and the use of any available knowledge of other investigations or excavations close by. In the case of existing records, accounts must be taken of any changes which might have been induced by recent mining and any changes in the use of groundwater. Groundwater abstraction or recharge changes can affect the accuracy of previous records.

The engineer must consider existing records and geology in conjuction with a project before he can recommend the need for a particular site investigation to his client. His proposal will usually be for a preliminary exploration and the determination of a few necessary properties from which he can then assess the need for, and nature of, an investigation to establish a cost-effective evaluation of the soil properties and groundwater regime. In these assessements the engineer should also give consideration to the information needed by the contractor. Despite the use of many boreholes and tests there is still the likelihood of the soil conditions changing between boreholes. The cost-effectiveness of the site investigation is therefore the art of deciding just how much information should be obtained at what cost to minimize the possibility of later changes and the additional costs that would be incurred. Any claim by the contractor for encountering ground circumstances which could not be reasonably foreseen is usually an outcome of the decision on the extent of the site investigation to be undertaken or made available to him.

The engineer has a responsibility to base his designs on sound criteria and to assess ably the construction proposals of the contractor. He must provide the contractor with adequate data to assess possible alternative methods of construction unless he has decided to use a particular method. For the assessment of the economic cost of excavation and construction below ground level the contractor needs to assess the costs of all the stages concerned. These usually include excavation, groundwater con-

Table 1. Ground conditions

Soil classification	General grading	Description
Cobbles and boulders	> 50mm dia.	Coarse, non-cohesive deposits whose characteristics can be visually assessed
Coarse gravels	50-20mm	
Medium gravels	20-6mm	Often found with some clay, as in hoggin
Fine gravels	6-2mm	Can be excavated with a spade
Well graded sands	Size distribution 2-0.05mm	When dry have little if any cohesion between particles; usually found well compacted and require a pick to excavate
Coarse sands	Uniform particles 2-0.5mm	
Medium sands	Uniform particles 0.5-0.2mm	Usually found in strata of different characteristics and sometimes colour; the finer sands are often slightly cemented; require a pick for excavation in lumps which can be abraded in the hand.
Fine sands	Uniform particles 0.2-0.05mm	

continued on facing page

Table 1 – continued

Silts	Mainly < 0.05mm	Have low plasticity and can be moulded by hand; particles difficult to identify visually; dry lumps have some cohesion but are easily powdered in the hand; organic silts are firmer than clayey silts; when damp silt is shaken, surface water appears
Clays	Finer than 0.002mm particles	Soft boulder and sandy clays are easily moulded in the hand; silty clays have a plasticine feel and can be moulded with firm pressure; fissured clays break into polyhedral fragments along the fissure planes and disintegrate under water
Peats	Fibrous material	Very compressible, open structured, soft; dark coloured and formed from decomposing or organic material
Mixed soils	Classified by the main particle size and the percentage by weight of material finer than 0.06mm; all cobbles and boulders are ignored in classification but their presence is noted	For meaningful classification, a representative number of samples should be examined

trol, support or cut-off systems for the side of the excavation, the construction of foundations or basements, the installation of services, back filling and restoration adjacent to the works. The effects of site and off site overheads for undertaking the operations and for the total period of construction, and the costs of any uncertainties or risks inherent in the proposals put to him must also be considered.

To assess and design construction methods for an excavation, groundwater control and any support system, the contractor will need to know the nature, strength and permeability of the different layers of the soil, the level at which the groundwater will be encountered and any information concerning fluctuations in that level for tidal or other reasons. It may be necessary to determine, by pumping tests, the permeability of the ground and the effect of a dewatering scheme installed in it. During the site investigation the drillers need to identify when groundwater is first detected during boring and variations in that level with time, possibilities of separate aquifers and significant variations in the properties of the different layers of soil. When sampling the strata, care is required to obtain representative samples and samples to be tested in a laboratory must be disturbed as little as possible.

Advice on the precautions to be taken in executing a site investigation to obtain representative results is given in British Standard code of practice CP 5930.[2]

Observations and disposal of groundwater

One of the quickest and most easily observed methods of determining the effects of high groundwater tables is to dig a trial pit or trench with an excavator and to pump from it. Observations can then be made of the upper soil strata, and the effect of water flowing out of the sides of the excavation, the likely instability which will result, the rate of inflow of the water and the time taken to establish an equilibrium. On sites expected to have variable soil conditions, it may be desirable to excavate a number of such holes to determine groundwater levels, the extent of rock outcrops or bands of peat. Where water movements are taking place across the site, such short excavations can give an indication, particularly with the use of dyes, of how the water is flowing.

When excavations are to be dewatered the water has to be disposed of in a way acceptable to the water authority and it may not be possible to pump it into the nearest stream or sewer. The acceptable method of disposal may depend on the extent of contamination by suspended solids, chemical or biological contents. In extreme circumstances, the contractor may have to pump from an excavation and discharge on to the ground behind a bund as far away as possible, hoping to dewater the excavation by pumping the water out faster than it can return.

When the pumping of water from or around a new excavation could draw down a groundwater table under adjacent building or other works, the soil properties adjacent to these works should also be investigated so that measures may be taken to avoid damage which might result from changes in the groundwater conditions.

Groundwater flows

When considering an excavation three aspects of

groundwater require attention. It is necessary to determine how water is present in the soil, how it will be replenished as pumping proceeds and how the properties of the soils within and around the boundaries of the excavation are likely to be affected. It is necessary to estimate the rates of ingress of water into the excavation both initially and as pumping proceeds. A high cost of pumping to lower the water table is likely to influence which construction method is chosen. This must be assessed in conjunction with the costs of excavation and the use of a coffer-dam or other groundwater control systems. The engineer originating the design may need to take into account such factors to produce a practical and economic scheme. An early judgement as to the nature and scale of the investigation required into the groundwater conditions is necessary before design decisions are irrevocably taken.

Soil permeability

Permeability is the characteristic of a soil which governs the rate of flow through the interconnected pores and is therefore a function of particle size and soil grading. Granular soils essentially of sand or gravel are permeable and groundwater will pass freely through them; their permeability increases with the grain size. Clays are impermeable although water may seep slowly through sand or silty inclusions or from saturated fissures, so that an apparently dry face of clay might shortly become wet and possibly unstable. The quantities of water passing through clay will be predictably small. Silts allow the passage of water but are difficult to control by normal pumping methods as their permeability is low. Rocks have low permeability in the solid but usually pass water through jointing planes and faulted zones which may cause instability problems.

The predictability of these soil types becomes complex when they are mixed. The presence of clay or silt in a sand or gravel can result in strata of varying permeability for which it is difficult to predict how groundwater will flow. It may give rise to strata of preferential drainage characteristics or of perched water tables. The presence of clay intrusions in rock formations can also complicate assessments of water flow and the stability of exposed surfaces. The use of boreholes to identify ground conditions is usually necessary for the assessment of subsoil conditions. A special investigation of groundwater conditions may involve the use of geophysical methods.

The coefficient of permeability is expressed in metres per second. Typical values are shown in Table 2. The

Table 2. Permeability of soils

Soil type	Coefficient: m/s
Gravel	$> 10^{-1}$
Coarse sand	$> 10^{-2}$
Silty fine sand	$> 10^{-5}$
Silt	$> 10^{-6}$
Clays	$< 10^{-7}$

permeability of a soil can be determined by the following methods in decreasing order of the reliability

(a) a pumping test from a well while the drawdown in the level of groundwater in observation wells or piezometers at different distances is observed

(b) rising and falling head permeability tests in soil investigation boreholes

(c) assessment from the inspection of particle size distribution curves; this is usually based on Hazen's formula for single grain size filter media and is less reliable when soil is less uniformly graded

(d) laboratory tests on representative undisturbed soil samples; the less representative or more disturbed the sample is, the less reliable the result will be

(e) assessment made on representative samples by suitably experienced geotechnical or dewatering staff.

More details of these methods and the calculation of flow rates to extraction wells are given in reference 1.

3. CONSEQUENCES OF DEWATERING OPERATIONS ON ADJACENT AREAS AND STRUCTURES

An excavation below the groundwater table will usually require the water within the excavation to be removed by a dewatering system. Such a system may involve using a pump within the excavation or providing a surrounding ring of dewatering wells or sumps. The rate at which water will flow through the ground into the dewatered area will be a function of the differential pressure head which is created and the permeability of the soils through which the water passes. Replenishment can come from water already in the ground, from adjacent water courses or the sea, from natural precipitation, from leaking services or from discharging drains. Once the water table has been lowered within the excavation an equilibrium is likely to be achieved and the rate of abstraction from then on may reduce to less than half of the earlier rate.

When surrounding ground is quite permeable, as in the case of gravels and coarse sands, the area affected by the pumping operation can be extensive and the quantities of water extracted high. This may result in finer particle-sized material being carried through the soil by the groundwater and if filters are not used to prevent it, these fine materials will be pumped out. This can induce consolidation and settlement of the soils which have lost these finer fractions unless the remaining coarser material maintains soil structure stability. It is also likely to result in an increase in the permeability of these soils which will exacerbate the situation. It is therefore important that properly graded filters are provided and maintained at all wells. Careful observation of discharge water from sumps and wells will quickly show when appreciable volumes of fine particles are being removed.

Where pockets of fine or silty material can be washed out, or chemical deposits leached out of the soil, voids may be created which can lead to collapse of the overlying ground and affect the integrity of pavements or structures above. Lowering the groundwater table beneath existing buildings can increase the effective overburden pressure. This would induce consolidating settlements which, if not uniform, could damage those buildings or structures. These consolidating settlements can also significantly increase the loads in piles by inducing down drag. Such increases in pile loads may have unpredictable effects unless detailed records are available regarding the pile types, their lengths and the ground strata to which they transfer their loads by end-bearing and/or side friction. Dewatered soils may settle away from the underside of pile caps or ground slabs which without direct ground support may redistribute their imposed loads between the structural members at ground level.

Precautions should therefore be taken to avoid damaging adjacent buildings and works. Safety can be achieved by working within a coffer-dam, or other comparatively impermeable barrier, and limiting the pumping from the excavation side of that barrier so that the groundwater level outside it is not affected for very far. An alternative approach, particularly when the excavation is large, is to install a line of wells between the excavation and the adjacent works and to use these to top up or recharge the groundwater table at those points and prevent the dewatering at or around the excavation from affecting the ground below adjacent works (Fig. 1).

As a further demonstration of the effectiveness of this action, an observation or monitoring borehole can be provided alongside the existing works. The water for the recharging operation usually comes from the dewatering scheme. The steeper hydraulic gradient will mean that higher quantities of water are likely to be pumped than if recharging had not been adopted. Even when a recharge system is considered unnecessary it is a good idea to install observation boreholes alongside nearby structures to demonstrate that conditions under them are not being affected. Such observations can forestall many arguments and possible claims for alleged damage.

Dewatering operations which give rise to consolidation and settlement of adjacent areas can affect not only buildings and structures but also the integrity of pavements and services. The likely effect on road and similar pavements should be assessed to determine whether or not special safeguards are necessary. Adjacent areas should be checked for the precise locations and nature of any services therein. It is not sufficient to assume that services are exactly where they are shown on drawings; many do not appear on drawings so their locations should be checked on site. Electronic location detectors and dowsing methods can be used to find services.

Precautions should also be taken with regard to the operations of farms and other industries which have rights to operate boreholes or are dependent on natural lakes or water courses. The operation of a dewatering system has sometimes adversely affected such activities and the affected farms and industries have invoked injunctions and been awarded damages.

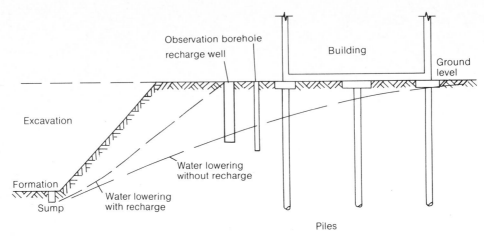

Observation borehole
recharge well

Building

Ground
level

Excavation

Water lowering
without recharge

Formation

Water lowering
with recharge

Sump

Piles

Fig. 1. Recharge system

4. SAFETY AND GROUNDWATER

The influence of groundwater on the safety of construction operations needs consideration in the case of excavations subject to groundwater flows or the stability of temporary works. When an excavation exceeding 1.2 m deep is undertaken, the construction regulations require that attention is paid to the hazards presented by possible collapse of the sides of the excavation. In practice this means that all excavations over 1.2 m deep, the sides of which are steeper than the natural angles of repose of the soils involved under saturated conditions, require protection

for people who work within or adjacent to them. When stability is dependent on a groundwater control system, that system should be designed and described in a construction method statement and the control methods defined.

To ensure that proper control is exercised over an excavation, the work should be supervised by a competent person. The works should be adequately protected to ensure the safety of passers-by. Safe means of access should be provided into and out of the excavation for all foreseeable conditions and particularly those pertaining to rapid flooding or loss of side stability caused by groundwater. There should be alternative means of escape from a potentially dangerous situation. All access ways, ladders and stairs must conform to the safety regulations. All statutory examinations should be carried out as defined in the regulations and recorded.

The construction method document should prescribe the sequence of support installation, excavation, operation within the excavation, backfilling and associated groundwater controls. The plant should, wherever possible, be positioned away from the edge of the excavation and operated in such a way that it cannot fall into the excavation. To ensure the safety and operating stability of pumps they should be located on stable soils, away from local accumulations of water, and restraining ties should be provided if necessary. Noise levels from the operation of pumps should not exceed permitted levels either during or outside normal working hours.

Before proposing the safe method of working, the area surrounding the proposed excavation should be examined for hazards such as

(*a*) the presence of existing services

(*b*) previously dug and backfilled service trenches which might induce collapse when the ground is removed adjacent to them

(*c*) perched water tables over impermeable layers (usually clay bands) which may suddenly be released to flow into the excavation.

(*d*) transmitted vibrations (such as those from traffic or piling) which might induce ground movements

(*e*) vertical cracks or fissures in impermeable soils (such as clays) which if filled with rainwater might cause the ground to collapse towards the excavation

(*f*) the presence of pockets of soft unstable soils behaving in a thixotropic manner.

It is valuable to keep records of all such discoveries, of the subsequent progress of the works and the reasons for any delays or deviations from the safe method of working statement.

When groundwater flows are prevented or diverted by the insertion of barriers, or locally increased by pump discharges, there may be consequences for the safety of temporary construction works such as falsework. In the design of falsework and other temporary structures account must be taken of the possibilities of groundwater movements affecting the support assumed to be provided by the underlying soils. The consequences of surface flood water as caused by extreme climatic conditions or interference with the previous provisions made to cater for excess water arriving on the site must also be taken into consideration.

5. DEWATERING SYSTEMS FOR CONTROLLING GROUNDWATER IN AND AROUND EXCAVATIONS

The dewatering of an excavation may be undertaken by pumping from sumps within it, from deep wells sunk around it, or by linked systems of wells or drains surrounding it with or without sophisticated methods to induce the water to flow to the pumps. The applicability of these methods is governed by the physical constraints of working space, the depth of the excavation below the groundwater table and the permeabilities of the ground strata. It may be desirable to undertake pumping tests to determine the severity of the problem and size of the dewatering equipment needed. It may also be necessary to combine one or more of these systems with geotechnical processes such as grouting or walling to obtain an economic solution to the problems presented during construction. The various dewatering processes and their range of applications to different soil conditions are shown in Table 3.

General comparisons

Dewatering systems

The selection of an appropriate dewatering system must take account of the plan dimensions and depth of the excavation. The influences of these are shown in Table 4. Table 5 indicates the suitability of the alternative systems to deal with differing quantities of water flow.

The choice of a dewatering system will be influenced first by the size and capacity of the system which affects the mobilization of plant and installation costs and second by the period for which it will be required to operate. The longer the period of operation the lower the weekly proportion of the establishment cost becomes, but the running costs of fuel, plant hire, supervisory staff, labour and maintenance accumulate steadily on a 24 hourly operational basis. This round the clock operation will not only entail supervision to deal with any breakdowns but may also require sound-reduction enclosures to meet the regulations governing the control of noise on construction sites. Guidance on what is necessary to reduce noise emissions to an acceptable statutory level is given in reference 3. The systems already referred to vary considerably in cost and can be graded by cost as shown in Table 6.

Pumping plant

The selection of pumping plant will be influenced by the quantity of water to be extracted and the height to which it must be pumped to ground level. It will also be influenced by the plant most readily available which could be used and the availability of suitable locations for it with any necessary sound insulation. The following types of pump should be considered

(a) *hand-lift diaphragm:* output from 1.1 m³/h for 32 mm suction, up to 14 m³/h for 100 mm suction; suitable for intermittent pumping in small quantities

Table 3. Application of groundwater lowering techniques

Soil type	Grading: mm	Permeability: m/s	Depth of effectiveness and use in soil types 4 m 8 m 12 m 16 m 20 m 24 m 28 m
Coarse gravel	60-20	> 1	
Medium gravel	20-6	> 1	
Fine gravel	6-2	$+ 10^{-1}$	
Coarse sand	2-0.5	$> 10^{-2}$	
Medium sand	0.5-0.2	$> 10^{-3}$	
Fine sand	0.2-0.05	$> 10^{-4}$	
Coarse silt	0.05-0.02	$> 10^{-5}$	
Medium silt	0.02-0.005	$> 10^{-6}$	
Fine silt	0.005-0.002	$> 10^{-7}$	
Clays	< 0.002	$< 10^{-7}$	

Water lowering techniques

Open sump drainage
Wellpointing
Wellpointing with vacuum
Electro-osmosis
Submerged pumps in wells
Deep wells with vacuum

13

Table 4. Plan dimensions and depth influences on selection of dewatering systems

Method	Depth limit	Width limit	Other limits
Sump pumping	Limits of excavation: up to 8 m below pump installation level; greater depth if a submersible pump is used	Increasing width increases requirement for sump and grip capacity	Shallow slopes may be required for unsupported excavations in silts and fine sands
Wellpointing	Maximum limit of drawdown for each stage: 3-4 m in silty fine sands, 5-5.5 m generally	Limited by soil cone of depression, R	Space required for unsupported side slopes
Horizontal wellpointing	Limits in installation below ground level: 4 m normally, 6 m maximum	Limited by cone of depression	A single pump will usually drain 220 m of 80 m pipe
Shallow wells	Limit of drawdown: 6-8 m below pump installation level	Not usually critical but the wider the excavation the more wells are required; limited then by soil cone of depression, R	
Deep wells	Unrestricted using submersible pumps	Not usually critical but the wider the excavation the more wells are required	Extremely large excavations may require ancilliary wells in centre of excavation
Eductor wellpointing	Unlimited but for wellpoint type drawdown usually restricted to 30 m	Related to depth and range of drawdown	
Electro-osmosis	Limits of excavation: 8 m below pump installation level; any depth in stages or with Eductor wellpoint systems	Not critical	Available power supply from mains or generators

(*b*) *motor-driven diaphragm:* output from 11 m^3/h for 50 mm suction up to 23 m^3/h for 100 mm suction; good solids handling capabilities; up to 40 mm for 100 mm models ideal for continuous pumping duties of sludge and silty water

(*c*) *pneumatic and hydraulic sump pumps:* air at 6 bar pressure gives outputs from 20 m^3/h against a 30 m head up to 70 m^3/h against a 3 m head; hydraulic oil at 140 bar and 34 l/min will give outputs of up to 100 m^3/h against a 3 m head; both useful for intermittent pumping on sites where either air or hydraulic supplies are available; limited solids handling capabilities.

(*d*) *self-priming centrifugal:* widely used for continuous pumping duties on site; outputs range from 17.5 m^3/h for 37.5 mm suction to 470 m^3/h for 200 mm suction; useful for handling solids up to 50 mm but abrasive materials can cause excessive wear on the impeller after long periods of pumping.

(*e*) *electric submersible:* outputs from 15 m^3/h for 32 mm discharge against a 10 m head up to 180 m^3/h for a 100 mm discharge against a 100 m head; these pumps are light and compact and handle dirty and abrasive water efficiently

(*f*) *rotary displacement (monopump):* can deal with considerable quantities of silt and sand; also used as a borehole pump; output for a 75 mm pump is 34 m^3/h against a 6 m head.

To make an accurate assessment of the likely costs of alternative dewatering schemes it is necessary to have reasonably reliable borehole data with no obvious

Table 5. Capability to deal with water flows

Sump pumping	Can cope with any flow but with high flows a danger of soil erosion (typical 150 mm pump capacity of 300 m^3/h)
Wellpoints	A single wellpoint handles between 4 and 0.6 m^3/h depending on soil type; for a 120 m length (40 at 3 m centres) flow is therefore between 160 and 24 m^3/h
Horizontal wellpointing	Determined by capacity of piping — up to 150 mm can be used
Shallow wells	Depends on diameter of borehole and quality of suction pump. A 300 mm borehole pump moves 400 m^3/h and a 150 mm borehole pump 200 m^3/h
Deep wells	Depends on diameter of borehole and quality of suction pump. A 300 mm borehole pump moves 400 m^3/h and a 150 mm borehole pump 200 m^3/h
Eductor wellpointing	Usually where flow is low or very low
Electro-osmosis	Only where flow is low, where k $\leqslant 10^{-9}$ m/s

Table 6. Relative costs of alternative methods of groundwater exclusion

Method	Cost approximation (based on typical 1985 rates)
Sump pumping	Cheapest; mainly the cost of hiring pumps; a 100 mm pump with 30 m discharge costs about £90 per week
Wellpointing	Very competitive for reasonable length excavations to moderate depth over short period; a set of 40 at 3 m centres would cost to hire including the pump, about £180 per week; disposable wellpoints are cheaper for long-term projects
Horizontal wellpoints	Expensive; only competitive in the very long term; £1500 minimum mobilization charge; costs about £8 per linear metre to install plus a hire of £5 per day per 100 m using 100 mm pump
Shallow wells	More expensive than wellpoints for the same depth; competitive on confined sites over a long hire below the limiting depth handled by wellpoints; some disposable types cheaper in the longer term
Deep wells	Relatively expensive depending on number installed, depth and strata; usually only economic for larger projects; a submersible pump (100 mm) costs about £30 per linear metre; the well will cost about £10 per linear metre to sink
Eductor wellpointing	Very expensive; equivalent in cost to four stages of wellpointing; about £720 per week
Electro-osmosis	Very expensive

discrepancies between adjacent positions and particle size distribution curves for the soil strata, and then to consult specialists in dewatering. In many situations an engineer will make early broad decisions based on handbooks and experience available to him and progressively refine his selection as soils data becomes available. This will give a tendering dewatering specialist some confidence that his advice is being sought in the context of a likely design and solution and that minimal abortive proposals will be required from him.

Sump pumping

Sump pumping is the simplest method of groundwater control to install as it requires merely the positioning of a suitable pump at a hole or sump into which the water flows by gravity. In the case of an excavation one or more sumps will be dug and water flowing into the excavation will be intercepted by perimeter shallow trenches (grips) or drains with falls to the sumps. The intercepting grips may be dug at intermediate levels and progressively lowered. The sump may have been sunk to its final depth in one operation or may also be lowered progressively.

Wellpointing

A wellpoint installation comprises a number of small diameter strainers (wellpoints) usually about 50 mm in diameter and 0.5-1 m long, which are inserted in the surrounding ground to an excavation. These wellpoints are connected by vertical riser pipes, of not less than 40 mm bore, to a common suction header main (Fig. 2). This suction main is connected to the suction side of a vacuum-assisted self-priming centrifugal or piston pump. Thus the groundwater flows by gravity to the wellpoints and is drawn up by risers to be discharged by the pump.

The pump, which is usually a nominal 100 mm in diameter or larger, may be mobile for trenching operations or may be housed to serve for a long period on a large excavation project. In the case of linear operations such as trenching, the wellpoints may be installed as lines to be extended progressively; in other cases they are usually installed as a closed ring (Fig. 3).

The wellpoints are usually installed below the level to which the groundwater table is to be lowered. This may be formation level for the excavation, just into the top of an impermeable layer which extends down below formation level, or at the maximum operating depth of the vacuum-assisted wellpoint system. In the latter case the

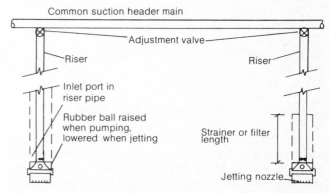

Fig. 2. Typical wellpoints

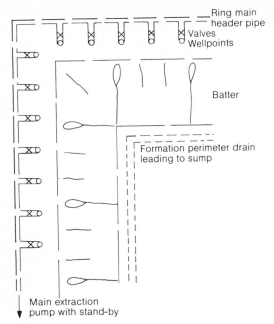

Fig. 3. *Wellpointing around the excavation*

excavation may comprise several levels of wellpoints (Fig. 4).

The spacing of the wellpoints depends on the permeability of the soils and is generally between 0.6 m and 3 m. The wellpoint system will usually be employed with an operating height of not more than 5 m. In marginal cases an engineer may decide to lower the level of the header main or accept some inflow at formation level in order to employ a single stage wellpoint system. As the wellpoint system intercepts the water flowing towards the excavation and the side slopes are freed from water it is possible with granular soils to employ much steeper side slopes than would be the case with sump pumping and so reduce the size of the excavation.

There are two types of wellpoint in common use. The first is the self-jetting wellpoint with a screen of perforated or slotted metal or plastic, about 50 mm in diameter at the lower end of a rigid riser pipe of slightly smaller diameter. The unit is jetted or wash-bored into the soil using a high pressure (13 bars) high volume (6.5 m^3/h) pump. In hard soils or soils with hard inclusions the holes may need preboring. This wellpoint is reusable. The second type of wellpoint is disposable, usually plastic, with a larger (65 mm) perforated strainer section connected to an unperforated smaller bore riser. The unit is installed in a larger (100 mm) liner tube previously jetted, or otherwise installed, into the soil. Disposable wellpoints are usually purchased rather than hired so that extensions of the pumping time will not increase the hire charge.

The performance of a wellpoint is enhanced by a surround of washed sharp sand placed around it and its riser. The extracted water should thus have minimal suspended solids but it is likely that flow conditions will vary considerably. Adjustment valves at the tops of the risers are used to regulate the extraction of water and air and minimize the air extracted as excess air reduces the efficiency of the system. The riser pipes of any one

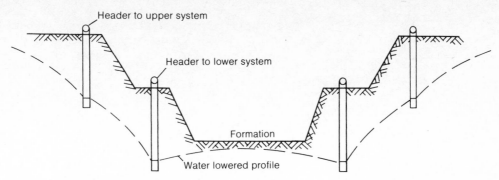

Header to upper system

Header to lower system

Formation

Water lowered profile

Fig. 4. Multi-stage wellpointing

system should be of the same length, and the header main and the suction intake of the pumping set should be at the same level. Fig. 5 shows a typical installation.

The rate of pumping for any set of circumstances can be computed using Dupuis or similar methods, or assessed from experience. The initial rate of extraction is likely to be about twice the equilibrium rate of pumping. It is common practice to use two pumps initially and then continue using one pump at a time with the second available as a stand-by.

Horizontal wellpointing

There are two types of horizontal wellpointing, each of which has particular circumstances which make it a competitive solution. The first system involves the installation of horizontal continuous perforated plastic pipes, usually 80 mm in diameter, encased in a filter consisting of a woven nylon mesh at the required depth (not exceeding 6 m). These disposable collection pipes are connected to pumps on the surface by non-perforated plastic pipes. A single pump can usually drain 220 m of pipe. There are purpose designed and built trenching machines which, although large and expensive to hire, can install long lengths of drainage pipe quickly (e.g. in excess of 50 m/h in favourable conditions). When there are several permeable strata above the perforated pipe a granular backfill can be introduced above the perforated pipe to encourage drainage of the several strata while the trenching operation breaks up impermeable bands of soil. The ability to start pumping once the first length of pipe has been installed, usually on the first day of installation work, also makes the system attractive when unexpected groundwater problems arise.

The second system, the Ranney collector method, is

Fig. 5. Wellpointing at foot of an excavated slope

applicable when vertical wellpointing or bored wells cannot be used. In this system a lined shaft is sunk to a lower level than that for dewatering. From this shaft horizontal wells or perforated pipes are jetted or jacked through the usually saturated soil strata. These horizontal wells comprise outer and inner casings with the space between filled with gravel. Valves are installed where they pass through the shaft walls to control the inflow. Pumping from the shaft may be by pumps at the bottom or top of the shaft.

Shallow wells

Shallow wells comprise surface pumps which draw water through suction pipes installed in bored wells drilled by the most appropriate well drilling or bored piling equipment. The limiting depth to which this method is employed is about 8 m. Because wells are prebored, this method is used when hard or variable soil conditions preclude the use of a wellpoint system. These wells are used in very permeable soils when wellpointing would be expensive and often at inconveniently close centres. The shallow well can be used to extract large quantities of water from a single hole. When equilibrium is achieved the drawdown profile of the water table can extend a long way, so it is usual to install these wells lower than a wellpoint system, providing the suction head of the pump is not exceeded. In an extreme case the pump might be located a metre or so below ground level. Since the performance of such wells is difficult to predict, a pumping test is often performed on the first well with observation wells to gauge the drawdown profile.

Deep wells

When water has to be extracted from depths greater than 8 m and it is not feasible to lower the type of pump and suction piping used in shallow wells to gain a few extra metres of depth, then deep wells are sunk and submersible pumps installed within them. Again, a cased borehole can be sunk using well drilling or bored piling rigs to a depth lower than the required dewatered level. The diameter will be 150-200 mm larger than the well inner casing, which in turn is sized to accept the submersible pump. Alternatively, deep wells may be sunk using reverse circulation rigs that do not require boring casings.

When selecting positions and drilling equipment the possibility of ground settlement adjacent to the well should be considered in relation to the consequences on existing buildings or services. The inner well casing has a perforated screen over the depth requiring dewatering and terminates below in 1 m of unperforated pipe which may serve as a sump for any material which passes the filter. After the well casing has been installed it is surrounded by backfill over the unperforated pipe length and with graded filter material over the perforated length as the outer casing is progressively withdrawn. Particular care is needed during this operation. Before the pump is inserted, water is forced through the filter and any fines collecting in the sump section are removed. A typical bored well is shown in Fig. 6.

The grading of the filter material must be appropriate for the soil to be dewatered and this will be determined from the grading analysis of the soil, usually using the Terzaghi rule.[4] In the more permeable soils the wider in-

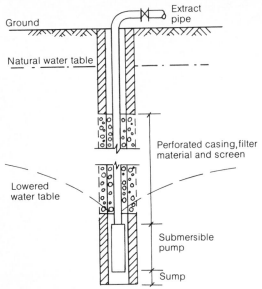

Fig. 6. Typical deep well

Labels in figure: Ground; Natural water table; Lowered water table; Extract pipe; Perforated casing, filter material and screen; Submersible pump; Sump

fluence of the deep well set far below the required dewatered level enables the wells to be widely spaced, whereas in less permeable soils the limited influence requires more closely spaced wells, which nevertheless extract far less water and so make use of smaller capacity pumps. As with shallow wells the initial pumping may involve twice the volumes when equilibrium is achieved. It is not usual to provide 100% stand-by capacity just one or two pumps to replace pumps under maintenance or repair.

The failure of any pump should not jeopardize the dewatered excavation and the adjacent wells should be capable of attracting much of the water normally extracted by the non-operational well under equilibrium conditions. When the pumps are supplied with power from a common source, such as mains electricity or a single generating set, a stand-by power supply should be available.

Eductor wellpointing

Eductor wellpoint systems are used mainly in North America (rarely in Britain), and a variation on conventional wellpointing. Instead of employing a vacuum to draw water to the wellpoints, the eductor system uses high pressure water and riser units, each about 30-40 mm in diameter. As shown in Fig. 7, a high pressure supply main feeds water through a venturi tube immediately above the perforated well screen, creating a reduction in pressure which draws water through the well screen and up through the large diameter riser pipe. The high pressure main feeds off the return water. The advantage of the eductor system is that in operating many wellpoints from a single pump station, the water table can be lowered in one stage from depths of 10-45 m. However, the wellpoints and mains are more expensive and the efficiency of such systems is lower than that of other pumping schemes. They become economically competitive at depth in soils of relatively low permeability.

Electro-osmosis

The methods already described are used with granular

soils and the inclusion in these of clay and silt fractions reduces their permeabilities and extends the time to achieve equilibrium in the lowered groundwater condition. When these finer clay and silt fractions predominate, the capillary forces acting on the porewater inhibit free passage of the water under gravity to the point of extraction at a well. To achieve a useful flow the water must be encouraged; electro-osmosis is an extreme and expensive means of achieving it.

Anodes in the form of steel rods or thick pipes are driven into the perimeter soil around the excavation and are supplied with a direct current (usually 50-150 V) which passes to the water in the pores of the soil and causes the positively charged particles to move to the cathodes which are the filter wells, clear of the excavation. The groundwater is pumped from the filter wells. Water is thus drawn directly from the sloping sides of the excavation, stiffening the soils and enabling steeper slopes to be used.

The considerable use of electricity (0.5-14 kW/m³ of dewatered soil) and the cost of replacing the anodes as they corrode makes the system comparatively expensive. The anodes and cathodes are usually separated by about 6 m and are sometimes used in patterns so that several anodes supply charged water to a single cathode. As the very fine capillaries in such soils are drained of water they shrink and the ground consolidates and becomes stabilized. It enables pumps to be turned off for routine maintenance without the need for immediate replacement

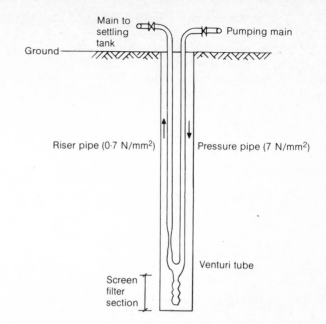

Fig. 7. Typical eductor wellpoint

to avoid the loss of equilibrium, which is a risk with other systems. Electro-osmosis can be employed only on these very fine grained strata; a conventional groundwater control system should be used on more permeable strata to give an economic solution.

6. DEWATERING SHALLOW OPEN EXCAVATIONS

The cheapest excavation costs are often obtained by the use of open cut excavation methods when stable side slopes can be provided around the excavation. A preliminary assessment of the ground condition can be made using the criteria in Table 1 to determine the soil type. From Table 7 the safe angles of repose for stable side slopes can be selected, depending on whether the slopes are going to be essentially dry, or subject to continuing seepage towards the slope. A dry slope will exhibit no more than minor seepage from the excavated side slopes. Soft clays are frequently stronger within a few metres of ground level due to drying out. The clay crust is fissured for the same reasons, although the fissures may not be visible. Fissuring will cause an unstable face if the face is cut at too steep an angle to the horizontal. Care needs to be exercised when softer clays underlie stiffer soils which may themselves be stable at steeper slopes. Table 7 should be interpreted such that selected angles of repose are no steeper for the upper layers of soil than they are for the lower ones.

The presence of high water table makes it necessary to assess how best to remove the water within and entering that excavation without jeopardizing side stability or causing heave of the formation. It is good practice to prevent surface water around the excavation from running into it. When excavating through rocklike or cohesive ground it is possible to excavate with steep side slopes, but continued stability may decrease due to water emerging through fissures or other thin permeable layers.

Should such emerging water remove fines or build up local confined water pressures, the stability of the slope could be jeopardized. Care is therefore needed in continued inspection of the sides of excavations for water movements and changes.

By adopting a cautious approach and accepting the entry of side water into an excavation, sump pumping can be used to remove that water by collecting it from around the formation. When a permeable stratum overlies an impermeable stratum in which the excavation is founded it is possible to form a berm at the top of the impermeable stratum and collect the water at that level.

Even when permeable strata extend to formation level it is possible to employ open cut excavation and sump pumping. With a low head of water above formation level the water surface is depressed towards the pumping sump, the seepage lines do not emerge on the sloping face, and the natural angle of repose gives a stable slope (Fig. 8). When the water table rises to give a greater head or if the side slopes are steepened, the seepage lines will emerge from the sloping face giving rise to instability (Fig. 9). As the seepage lines come closer together the velocity of the seepage water increases and possible washing out of material and localized collapse may occur. To accept the greater water head, the side slopes should be flattened and blanketed with graded filter material or a proprietary system which will pass the water but retain the soil in position if it is fine and likely to be eroded.

Table 7. Safe temporary slopes

Soil description	Safe temporary slopes: degrees from horizontal	
	Dry site	Wet site
Boulders	35-45	30-40
Cobbles	35-40	30-35
Gravel	30-40	10-30
Sand	30-35	10-30
Silt	20-40	5-20
Soft clay		
Cut 1.2-3 m deep	30-45	10-20
Cut 3-6 m deep	20-30	
Firm clay		
Cut 1.2-3 m deep	30-45	20-25
Cut 3-6 m deep	30-40	
Stiff clay		
Cut 1.2-3 m deep	40-45	25-35
Cut 3-6 m deep	35-45	
Mixed soils	Dependent on soil category as characterized by finer constituents	
Peat		
Soft non-fibrous	10-20	5-10
Firm non-fibrous	15-25	10-15
Firm fibrous	35-40	20-25
Stiff fibrous	35-45	25-35
Rock	According to orientation of planes	

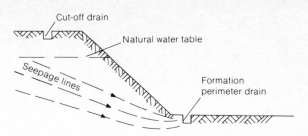

Fig. 8. Open excavation with stable slopes

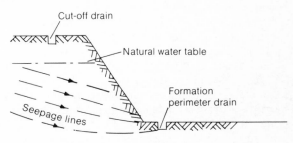

Fig. 9. Open excavation with unstable slopes

When permeable strata extend under the formation there is a strong risk of instability of the formation shown by heave of any overlying impermeable strata or boiling of small grained permeable strata. This can be countered by pumping from pits or stand-pipes within the formation area (Fig. 10).

25

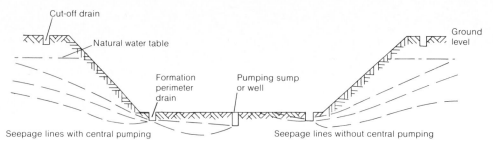

Cut-off drain

Natural water table

Ground level

Formation perimeter drain

Pumping sump or well

Seepage lines with central pumping

Seepage lines without central pumping

Fig. 10. Central pumping for control of formation

In a rock excavation the extracted water is likely to contain few suspended solids, but with softer soils the proportion of suspended solids will increase. It is necessary to consider the origin of those suspended solids and whether their extraction should be avoided. The nature of the extracted water will also affect the siltation of the interception grips and the sumps and will influence the selection of the pump drawing water from the sump.

The grips or drains should be designed and constructed with due care so that they neither undermine the toes of the side slopes to the excavation nor require excessive maintenance. Their installation should take into consideration the working space around the permanent works, the cost of any increase in space which the drains might entail and what is to be done with the drains when their purpose has been served. When the sumps are used for an extensive period it is good practice to line them with pipes, timber or concrete, or to fill with granular materials.

In permeable soils, when space around the neat size of the formation is limited and side slopes have to be made as steep as is practicably stable, water must be prevented from entering the excavation. It is intercepted by a ring of either wellpoints or shallow wells located around the excavation (section 5). The use of wellpoints or shallow wells to dewater the ground will be economic if it enables the use of steeper sides to an excavation and a smaller overall size. Providing the wellpoints and shallow wells are taken deep enough they can lower the water table below formation level. However, it may still be economic to install pumping points on the formation, particularly in wide excavations where even surrounding deep wells may not effectively control groundwater across the formation.

The soil conditions and the size of the excavation determine the method of dewatering, but the method of excavation and the construction of subsequent works on the formation should also be considered when the excavation plant may only be operated within the excavation with provision of access for the removal of excavated material from one end. When the plant stands at ground level no ramp is needed for the removal of spoil, but otherwise provision must be made for the ramp and groundwater control to extend beyond the excavation at some point, unless alternative mucking out arrangements are made for the last section to be dug.

The construction of concrete foundations within the excavation frequently involves the use of cranes which may be confined to single or tracked locations, or may be mobile. The effectiveness of the cranes is reduced as their radius of operation increases. The location of a crane around or within the excavation may therefore involve an economic balance between the size and cost of the crane, measures to reduce the overall width of the side slope of the excavation, the cost of excavation by alternative methods and the benefit of a local support to the crane by piling in certain locations. Such piling might be local sheet piling or a piled platform.

The use of transport within the excavation requires that the formation is protected against damage. This can be achieved by providing a strong layer of blinding concrete or by a temporary road above formation level and trimming to formation as late as possible. While construction operations proceed it is important to protect and maintain all parts of the dewatering system and to be alert to changes in the quantity of water being abstracted and the suspended solids within it.

The method of backfilling around the structure must be able to resist applied loads and the effects of the dewatering system being removed. Walls must resist applied loads and the structure must be secure against flotation. In exceptional cases when the structure has been designed for groundwater to enter into a collection system from which it is permanently abstracted, it is necessary to determine at the start of the work when the permanent arrangements take over the duties of the contractor's temporary dewatering system.

These conditions apply when shallow excavations are undertaken in an open cut excavation. When this option is precluded a perimeter support system will be selected from the alternatives described in section 8. For deeper excavations such support systems will extend right round the excavation, whereas in shallow excavations they may be required around only part of the perimeter if that is an economic solution and if ramped access into the excavation is used.

7.   TRENCH EXCAVATIONS

Trench excavations are probably the commonest and yet potentially most dangerous excavations because of their narrow width to depth proportions. Groundwater conditions and flows are usually difficult to predict and their variability along such a linear excavation requires constant alertness by an appointed supervisor.

Groundwater control is used to stop or reduce the groundwater flow into a trench where the water table is high, and to reduce uplift pressures at the bottom of the trench. The width and depth of the trench to be excavated, the length of trench to be open at any one time and the rate of advance of the trenching operation will, together with the permeability of water-bearing soils, determine the amount of dewatering equipment required to achieve the necessary drawdown of the groundwater table. Most trenches will have side support systems to provide safe working conditions. These support systems will be of one of the following

(*a*) continuous sheet piling or trench sheeting
(*b*) discontinuous trench sheeting
(*c*) proprietary excavation boxes
(*d*) timbering.

Guidance for the selection of an appropriate method is given in references 5 and 6.

Two principal methods are used to dewater trenches up to 6 m deep — sump pumping and wellpointing. The effectiveness of each method will depend on the nature of the soil, the proportions of the trench and the drawdown of groundwater required. The ranges of soils in which various methods may be used are as given in Table 3.

Sump pumping

Sump pumping is simple and cheap to install and can be used in a wide variety of soil conditions. It can be used in association with either open-jointed sheeting or close sheeting. Its main disadvantage is that the water flows into the trench and thus may cause instability of the trench bottom from upward seepage. Sump pumping also involves the risk of the fine constituents being removed from the soil and hence erosion or undermining. If this happens, alternatives to sump pumping should be considered. It is essential to keep water flows to a minimum in the base of the trench and to surround the suction hose inlet with a graded filter. The delivery side of the pump should be monitored by taking samples of water and checking the proportion of fines being removed.

Continuous sheeting is installed at the trench sides when the soils are very permeable to provide continuous support to the excavated faces and to control the rate of water entering the trench. Sump pumping is used to remove that water (Fig. 11). The continuous sheeting should be driven well below the formation level to lengthen the drainage path and to provide stability each side of the trench formation. The sump is usually located to one side of the trench and often consists of an open pipe surrounded by gravel. Sump pumping is also used with discontinous trench sheeting and when the soil is of low permeability so that only small quantities of water enter the trench. In these cases the depth of the sheeting below formation level will be determined from the design of the trench sheeting system to support the excavated faces of the trench safely.

Wellpointing

Wellpointing is usually installed to extract the water

from the ground before the trench is excavated and hence avoid instability of the excavated faces caused by water emerging through them. The method depends on the permeabilities of the soil layers and the requirements for access to the trench. It may entail either a single-sided system with the wellpoints and their header pipe installed along one side of the trench only, or a double-sided system with wellpoints and connecting header pipe on each side of the trench.

The single-sided system is preferable as it requires fewer wells, less pipework and lower installation costs and only interferes with access to one side of the trench. A double-sided system is installed when a single-sided row of wellpoints will not depress the water table on the far side of the trench sufficiently to stablize the sides and bottom of the trench against water movements. It is occasionally necessary to use a double-sided rather than a single-sided system when any header pipe system must be kept away from the trench to permit plant work adjacent to it on either side of the trench.

The length of dewatering system operated at one time is determined by the economics of equipment hire, the length which can be controlled by a single pump, and the time required to install and obtain satisfactory performance from the system by comparison with the rate of advance of the trenching operations (Fig. 12).

Wellpointing is normally carried out by specialists whose advice should be sought about assessing the need and the selection of the appropriate system. Wellpoints are commonly used in sands and mixed soils containing sands. In more permeable soils, such as gravels, far larger

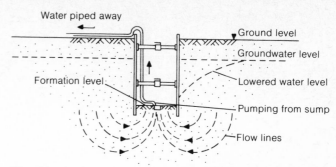

Fig. 11. Typical detail of sump pumping in trench

quantities of water may need to be abstracted, which would mean wellpoints at uneconomically close centres. They are usually installed at 0.6-3 m centres. In clay soils the rates of seepage are usually too small for the effective operation of a wellpoint system. The performance of the system in mixed soils will be affected by variations of permeability between pockets and layers of particularly permeable or impermeable soils.

Single-sided wellpoint systems

Single-sided wellpoint systems are mostly used for economy and speed. They are installed between the trench and the proposed line of deposition of the trench excavated material so that free access is available to the trench from the other side. The header pipe is usually located just below original ground level to minimize damage and gain a little more suction on the system. It is

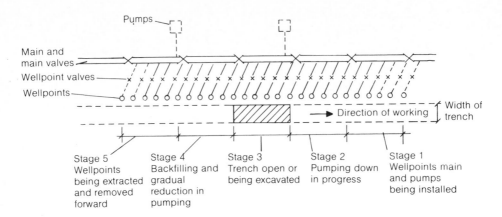

Fig. 12. Progression of wellpointing to a trench

important to provide hazard-free conditions along the working areas each side of the trench. Sometimes it will be economic to lower the ground level almost to the original water table level along the trench route before installing the wellpoint system.

To be economic and effective the soil conditions should be no more permeable than those of sands and should establish the required drawdown of the groundwater level in three days. If this is not achieved then additional measure may be necessary such as the use of vertical sand drains to improve the drawdown on the far side of the trench, or the installation of such drainage in the trench formation (Figs 13 and 14).

Double-sided wellpoint systems

For wide or deep trenches and for soils with variable permeabilities in different layers or regions, it may be necessary to install a wellpoint system along each side of the trench. Such double-sided systems restrict access to the trench and may require the header pipes to be lowered and covered on at least one side.

It may become necessary to employ larger capacity plant to increase the ability to handle loads at a greater radius with adequate margins of safety. Double-sided systems can cope with mixed ground conditions far more effectively than single-sided systems and for their additional cost provide an ability to cope with unexpected

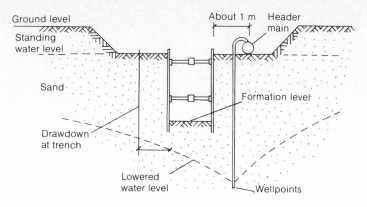

Fig. 13. Single-sided wellpoints in freedraining soils

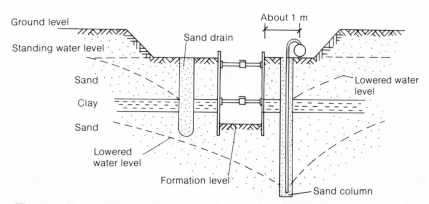

Fig. 14. Single-sided wellpoints with impermeable stratum

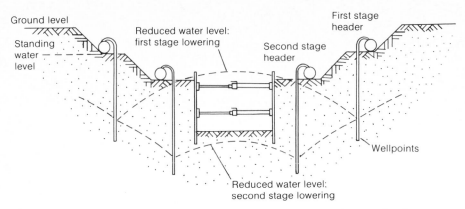

Fig. 15. *Multi-stage system of wellpointing. (Reduction of water level per stage varies from 2 m to more than 6 m depending on soils and efficiency of the total pumping system)*

groundwater behaviour and usually a faster drawdown to an equilibrium condition.

When the groundwater requires lowering to a level too deep for a system installed at or near to ground level to cope, then providing there is space for them, additional systems can be installed at lower operational levels as shown in Fig. 15. It may be economic to deal with a short length of such a deep trench but continuous sheeting or other methods may be preferable for dealing with restricted access or local ground stability.

8. EXCAVATIONS USING GROUND SUPPORT SYSTEMS

Ground support systems are used for deep excavations, for excavations adjacent to existing structures, pavements and services, and for others where the use of sloping sides to the excavation is not acceptable or economic. These support systems are usually walls which may be permeable or impermeable to groundwater and which are installed ahead of the main excavation work to provide protected working spaces or coffer-dams. Such walling systems must resist the external pressures of the soil conditions and any applied loads either by acting as free-standing cantilevers, the use of internal strutting or by the use of external ground anchors. The strutting and anchoring are inserted when the excavation reaches appropriate depths within the coffer-dam.

There are a number of alternative methods which can provide this temporary side support and the selection must take into account a number of factors including that of the groundwater conditions[7, 8](see Figs 16-18).

Sheet piled walls

A closed cell of interlocking steel sheet piles provides an impermeable wall around the coffer-dam if driven into an impermeable soil stratum. When this is not possible the lines of seepage flow vertically down behind the sheeting and up into the excavation. This causes instability and a formation of fine grained soil which may boil if sufficiently high velocities of flow arise. In such cases, and when there is an excessive artesian pressure below an impermeable layer at the formation, the groundwater must be stopped from disrupting the formation. Otherwise the excavation must be undertaken in the wet with a trémied concrete plug placed underwater to resist the water pressure until the concrete has matured and the water level can be lowered. To preclude appreciable quantities of groundwater from flowing into the coffer-dam it is usual to sink wells, sufficient in number and depth to intercept the seepage lines, below the toe level of the piling. When the expected inflow of water is comparatively small it may be sufficient to pump from the coffer-dam from a sump at current excavation level until 0.5 m above formation, and then sink wellpoints or sumps adjacent to the sheet piling to lower the water level the necessary remaining amount.

When the external groundwater control system of deep wells is to be maintained, then for a deep coffer-dam the design of the sheet piling and its supports may be based on lower external pressures using drained soil parameters rather than saturated ones. In some instances it may be economic, even when the sheet piles are toed into an impermeable soil strata, to lower the groundwater outside the coffer-dam by a dewatering system for a more stable ground surface while reducing the hydrostatic pressures to be resisted by the piling and its supports. To monitor the groundwater level outside the sheet piling, small holes are often drilled at the levels of permeable layers; the removal of plugs will indicate whether or not the layers have been drained. In difficult driving conditions for the sheet piling, such as compacted gravels and boulders in clay, not only are the pile heads liable to be damaged but also piles can be declutched as a pile is deflected off line. Apart from the immediate driving difficulties, this impairs the impermeability of the sheet piling making it necessary either to grout the soils behind the gap or to seal the piling on the inside by welding steel bars or plates to the inside face of the piling.

Only rarely is the sheet piling incorporated into the permanent works. It cannot be extracted if it is not free of the permanent works. The separation of the permanent

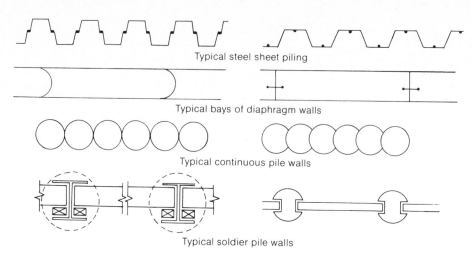

Fig. 16. Typical ground support systems

works and the piling is usually provided as working space for construction of the permanent works and incorporates a drain or grip to collect any water entering the coffer-dam. After the sheet piling has been extracted it must be expected that groundwater will be uniformly in contact with the permanent works to the full depth. Sheet piled walls are rarely used at depths exceeding 20 m. Sheet piled coffer-dams are used when a permanent external drainage and/or waterproofing membrane is specified for the outside of the perimeter walls to the permanent works. Such permanent drainage provision may be provided by hollow blocks or proprietary sheet drainage materials and the water extracted from a drainage pipe at the lower level. Co-ordination is needed between any temporary construction dewatering provisions and the operation a permanent system. Fig. 19 shows a combination of sheet piling and wellpointing and Fig. 20 shows relief pumping from a coffer-dam.

Diaphragm walling

Diaphragm walls are of cast in situ reinforced concrete or precast reinforced concrete inserted into a trench excavated through a bentonite slurry which supports the sides of the trench. It is common for this massive con-

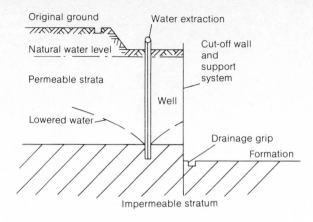

Fig. 17. Water lowering, upper permeable strata

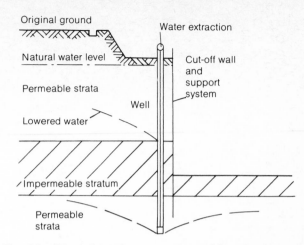

Fig. 18. Water lowering, two permeable strata

struction, not usually less than 600 m thick, to be incorporated into the design of the permanent works as a perimeter wall and part of a load bearing foundation.

The bentonite slurry is formulated with appropriate specific gravity for the soil conditions to maintain the stability of the trench faces during the excavation process and to cake those surfaces. The slurry inhibits local groundwater movements. Diaphragm walls will be permeable only if the joints are inadequately designed or there are faults in the construction of the wall. They can be constructed in most ground conditions and there is a choice of digging equipment to reach depths of over 60 m and for differing soil conditions. Diaphragm walls can be

installed close to existing buildings and, if incorporated into the design of the permanent works, can compete with sheet piled walls when there is sufficient wall area to justify high mobilization costs. They have the same stability requirements as sheet piled walls and the same considerations regarding groundwater flows apply. When the structural diaphragm wall is required over only the upper part of the depth required to cut off groundwater flow, the lower part may be provided as a slurry concrete or a grout curtain may be used.

Continuous walls using bored piles

Continuous walls comprise bored piles which are in

Fig. 19. Wellpointing applied between excavation deepening and sheet piling

Fig. 20. Relief of artesian pressure by boreholes in a coffer-dam

contact over their full length. Alternate piles may be constructed ahead of infill piles which overlap them, or piles are cast sequentially so that each pile cuts slightly into the previous one. The result will be impermeable if the joints are all effective. Such walls using continuously reinforced piles are often incorporated into the design of the permanent works as retaining walls to underpasses and similar structures. Any leaks may be sealed by grouting behind them. The walls act to resist groundwater flows in the same way as sheet piled and diaphragm walls.

Soldier pile walls

The wall systems already described should provide impermeable cut-offs to the lateral flow of groundwater. A cheaper permeable ground support system can be used with coarse grained soils which would not be washed out with groundwater as it passes through the wall. A soldier pile wall consists of universal steel beams or side slotted concrete members set into prebored vertical holes at about 3 m centres. The piles act as cantilevers or are strutted or anchored for stability.

As the excavation proceeds horizontal planks or sheeting are inserted between these members to distribute the loads of the retained external soil to the soldier piles. The use of soldier piles implies that the inflow of water will be controlled down the face of the wall to a collection drain below. This method can be used with soils which are predrained by an external ring of wells, but would not be used if uplift pressures could develop beneath the formation of the excavation. An advantage of the method is that the horizontal members can be progressively removed as backfilling is installed.

9.   GROUNDWATER AND ROAD CONSTRUCTION

In the design and construction of a road it is essential to achieve long-term stability of the formation beneath the road pavement and of the sides of cuttings and embankments. Water is the principle cause of damage to roads; it softens load bearing soils and can erode slopes. During construction it is necessary to excavate or fill to prepare profiled surfaces and to prevent deterioration of the soils exposed in those surfaces before effective long-term protection is provided. During road construction the route is much traversed by plant transporting bulk materials for the road and its associated structures and services. Temporary access roads and maintenance are usually needed to provide acceptable trafficking conditions for the plant and to avoid deterioration of the underlying soils from rainfall or the accumulation of water. The influence of groundwater and surface water movements on the design and excavation of cuttings, embankments, road formations and construction operations is now discussed. More detailed information is given in reference 9.

Cuttings

Although a cutting is a particular form of excavation in the ground having, at any time, either one or two open ends, it differs from most other excavations in that the side slopes become a permanent feature. Before a cutting is started, the water courses crossing and adjacent to the cutting, the likely movements of water emerging from porous strata as they are intersected by the excavation work, and the stability of the soils when exposed to the elements have to be investigated. The design of the cutting will incorporate diversions for water courses which will be affected and will also include special drainage provisions such as counterfort drains in the sloping faces to the cutting. The design will have a suitable slope to ensure long-term stability with ease of maintenance and minimal landtake.

In the construction of the cutting, the contractor will seek to provide the permanent protective measures as he proceeds, and to minimize additional temporary facilities except where these are necessary during the construction of the permanent measures. New drains will be installed for water courses at the original ground level and existing drains will be diverted to protect the excavated slopes from scour until the permanent protection has been provided. It may be necessary to drill into the exposed faces as the cutting is deepened, to intercept large inflows of water and divert them through drains to the bottom of the cutting to avoid heavy scour of the excavated face. When the cutting reaches formation level the toe drains should be installed in the correct positions, to avoid undercutting the side slopes and the required counterfort or other drainage systems in the excavated faces connected to them.

It is important to identify and release any accumulation of water behind the sloping faces which might lead to a sudden collapse. When the cutting is in a rock formation with steeply sloping side faces, regular inspections should be made to ensure that there is no risk of material falling from the face; precautions are needed against any identified hazards.

Embankments

Embankments are built up in compacted layers of suitable fill which is derived from excavations elsewhere along the route or brought in from borrow pits. It is essential that embankments are built with due regard to the nature of underlying soils and the changes in their condition which the surcharging load of the embankment is likely to cause. A significant increase in load from the construction of an embankment over saturated soft soils may lead to consolidation of these soils with the expulsion of excess pore water, or it might lead to rupture of the soil under and adjacent to the toes of the embankment so that heave occurs beyond the width of the embankment and existing adjacent water courses are disrupted.

It is usual when embankments are constructed over soft soils to provide a drainage layer before filling is started and to control the rate of filling in accordance with the dissipation of pore water pressures below. Alternatively, an unshaped embankment may be constructed, surcharged and left until equilibrium has been reached in the underlying soils, and only then trimmed to the final shape.

Systems of horizontal and vertical drainage paths can be installed to assist in the dissipation of excess pore water under embankments. The vertical system may be in the form of sand drains which are vertical columns of granular material installed in a pre-bored hole or in the form of wicks which consist of cardboard or plastic strips incorporating tubular channels which are installed by a driven mandrel. Horizontal drainage paths may be provided by a blanket of granular material, thick layers of geotextiles, horizontal wellpoints or agricultural drains.

Road formations

In the design of a road a relationship is established between the anticipated traffic loading and the supportive properties, expressed as the California bearing ratio, of the soils in the prepared formation. The thicknesses of sub-base, base and road pavement are established in accordance with design notes such as Road Note 29[10] and the selection of materials will depend on the availability of suitable materials at the required rate of supply and a comparison of the costs of alternative specifications.

The performance of the selected specification depends on the road construction remaining stable and the underlying formation maintaining its integrity and value. Wherever practical, the water table should be prevented from rising to within 600 mm of the formation level. This may require the provision of drainage or the raising of the road construction using frost-resistant filling. Alternatively, the value ascribed to the California bearing ratio should be reduced in accordance with Road Note 29.

Whichever method is used the formation should be so shaped that any water arriving on it drains sideways to a collection drain. The formation should be sealed and waterproofed to inhibit water penetration and softening. The materials used within 450 mm of the road surface should also be resistant to damage from frost. When drains are provided under or adjacent to roads they should be of adequate size and provided with access pits or manholes for maintenance and to avoid the consequences of local settlements from blocked drainage flows.

Most of the drainage runs associated with roads are of porous or perforated pipes surrounded by a granular material which backfills the trench excavation. This material should be graded to allow the passage of water and support the trench sides without soil from the trench sides being washed in. It is quite common to use geotextiles around the granular fill to provide a permeable separation between the soils and the fill to prevent movement of the soil into the fill. Several proprietary drainage systems are now used which comprises porous flexible sheets incorporating drainage passageways within layers of geotextiles and plastic sheets. Such systems include findrains, stripdrains, cordrains and Trammel. Fig.21 shows two typical examples.

Construction operations

Efficient transport of materials about the site is important. The larger the units of plant used, and the faster they operate, the more economic the movement of materials will be. Movement on the site is affected by the soils at the running surface and their ability to accept fast traffic in adverse weather conditions as well as the selection of appropriate plant.

Tracked vehicles are very tolerant of the haul road surface and weather conditions but are more expensive to operate over long distances. Rubber-tyred vehicles need a prepared running surface to lessen damage as they traverse the surface. To keep the haul roads above any standing water level it is usual to give them a cross-fall to drain water from the surface and to operate the earthmoving plant in ways which avoid damage to formations or material intended for filling. Groundwater and surface water must be kept under control to obtain efficient earthmoving and prevent soil deterioration.

When haul roads traverse comparatively soft or water-softened soils, a layer of geotextile fabric can be spread over the route and suitable fill laid and compacted over it to provide a running surface. The geotextile will separate the fill from the soil without restraining water movements and will greatly reduce the maintenance of the running surface. The road will be able to adjust to local softening or settlement without loss of integrity because of the tensile strength of the geotextile and the restraint it offers to the road material. When the haul road is critical to movement about the site the incorporation of a geotextile membrane and drainage measures can be cost effective.

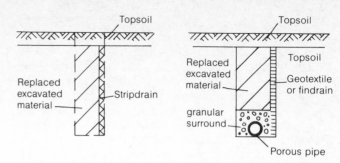

Fig. 21. *Typical drainage systems*

The fill used in a haul road is usually recovered for use in the works and sometimes the geotextile membrane can be reused.

The rapid detoriation of many soils in wet weather and the higher cost of operating earthmoving plant on wet soils limits most earthmoving operations to between March and October. In this period very wet spells can occur but there is an increasing probability that a combination of good earth-moving practices with greater rates of evaporation during the summer months will enable the exposed soils to dry and provide acceptable working conditions if they are left alone while wet. Many chalk formations, for example, become vulnerable when wet but dry off rapidly. This emphasizes the need to keep the surface soils well drained and clear of standing water.

Most underground excavations and tunnels are likely to be below a groundwater table and water will enter through exposed soil faces unless these are impermeable to flows. The cost of investigating the ground conditions adequately is sometimes prohibitively high and much use is made of a few boreholes and studies of available geological data. Whenever possible the design engineer will seek to locate his excavation within or adjacent to impermeable strata, but during construction careful control is needed with probing holes to identify the conditions ahead of the work. Water which flows under gravity through an exposed face is likely to destabilize the surface from which it emerges. Large continuing inflows of water pressure can quickly inundate the works and are a serious hazard.

To provide safety to these works and the operatives within them, protective linings are used, the soil stratum is probed and, where necessary, grouted ahead of a working face, or compressed air is used to counteract the hydraulic pressure. The protective linings may be permanent and in the form of tunnel segments, pipes, sprayed or cast concrete, or may be temporary and in the form of colliery arches or timbering. When conditions are soft and wet either a closed face tunnel machine is used with the excavated spoil removed as a slurry with bentonite or water, or the face of the excavation is excavated within compressed air.

The medical effects of working in compressed air can be harmful and the controls applied to those working in such conditions are strict. This makes such working conditions unattractive in economic as well as physical terms. The use of compressed air is being superseded by the development of the new closed face tunnelling machines.[8]

The flow of water from rock strata in which a tunnel is located will progressively remove the fine and often cementing material in bedding planes and fissures. Restraining the exposed rock with a tunnel lining system or rock anchors will counter the consequences of this. When it is required to prevent the movement of water out of the ground into the tunnel, a reinforced concrete lining is provided. This is initially installed with stand-pipes through it which transmit the main volume of water through the lining until the lining has matured and the stand-pipes are then grouted.

The flow of water through sands or other granular soils into an open tunnel face can be difficult to control and has led to the development of balanced earth pressure tunnel machines. These machines have a full tunnel section cutting face with holes for the injection of bentonite and the extraction of a displaced soil and bentonite mixture which is then pumped to the surface. Some machines can also crush small boulders. The use of such machines makes tunnelling independent of groundwater conditions. However, when it is not possible to use these machines the groundwater must be countered using grout ahead methods, partial wet face support or compressed air. The selected volume and pressure of compressed air ideally minimize the inflow of water and the outflow of

air. Adjustments are needed when either of these starts to increase.

When tunnelling without machines in clay soils, the excavated faces will usually appear dry when first exposed, but prolonged exposure in comparatively shallow tunnels may lead to weeping of these surfaces. This will be due to the exposed clay swelling, the fissures opening and permeability increasing to allow movement of pore water. Such swelling considerably increases the pressures on the temporary support system. In clay soils it is usual to employ drum diggers or pipe jacking methods which avoid temporary linings and lengthy exposure of surfaces, but this is often not possible in short runs, with small diameter tunnels or complex conditions when hand excavation is often the only method available.

Larger excavations for stations, bulk stores and shelters are excavated as progressive enlargements from a tunnel or heading which is reached by a shaft or sloping adit. A measure of the overburden conditions is thereby attained in the construction of the access which is frequently more difficult as it passes through variable strata (some connected to shallow water systems) before reaching the selected depth for the main excavation. The first horizontal bore provides more continuous assessment of the ground conditions along the length of the excavation. From this bore, the ground may be probed in the directions of enlargement to determine the measures necessary to ensure safe and economic excavation and lining for the enlargement. It is usual to try to provide cased holes leading into sources of water to reduce their effect on the strata near the excavation face and to lead the water away from the working faces to sumps for removal. Sometimes the incoming groundwater can be mixed with the spoil and the slurry pumped from the excavation.

Safety is a priority for the work as constructed and those working therein. Airlocks are often provided as a safeguard for emergency use of compressed air. Conditions around an excavation or tunnel may take time to reach equilibrium after all work has been completed and any compressed air turned off. This is because water movements can carry off silts and fine sands from pockets nearby and concentrations of salts (such as gypsum) may be leached from the soil and lead to subsequent settlements.

When excavating in soft soils the ground may be stiffened by the use of sophisticated special grout injection systems. Chemical grouts are available for most types of soft soil and can be injected systematically to provide a core of cohesive, watertight soil within which an excavation can be undertaken as supporting structures are installed. The soil conditions in France and Italy in particular have led to such methods being used most there.

Groundwater can be controlled around any excavation. However, in underground excavations the cost of groundwater control may be unacceptably high and the scheme abandoned in that location or that depth and moved to an alternative location.

11. MAKING USE OF GROUNDWATER DURING CONSTRUCTION

Difficulties in constructing foundations or other structures in saturated soils are caused by the combination of the soil and the saturating water. In most cases it is easiest to dewater the soil and to proceed in the dry within a stiff material or the surrounding wall provided by a ground support system. In unusual circumstances it is possible to reverse the process and to excavate below the groundwater table to produce a reservoir. Dredging is an example of this procedure. Construction within a water-filled excavation can then proceed using trémied underwater concrete within formers, or using precast concrete or prefabricated metal components. In extreme cases it is possible to float into position large structural units which have been built in the dry providing there is sufficient depth of water to allow them passage from the casting yard to their required position.

Soft or impermeable soil conditions in the formation of a coffer-dam can be disrupted by underlying water pressures resulting in boiling or heave of the formation. These conditions are often avoided by excavating in a flooded coffer-dam and placing a thick layer of trémied concrete over the formation. This method is often cheaper than deepening the coffer-dam or dewatering. Once the trémied concrete has set and is able by design to resist the uplift pressures, or is provided with controlling stand-pipes, the water is removed from the coffer-dam and work proceeds in the dry. In other cases a foundation is formed under water by trémied concrete within levelled forms and then precast concrete units are assembled on it

under water and the necessary connections made either mechanically or by in situ work. Using specially designed flowing concrete incorporating a suitable superplasticizer it is possible to fill quite complicated formers under water with assurance of homogeneity of the self-levelling concrete.

In submerged tube tunnel construction the route of a tunnel to be constructed in soft saturated soils is excavated by dredgers to form a canal. The sides of the canal may be lined with sheet piling to limit the width of the excavation or they may be formed at the natural angle of repose of the saturated soil. Sections of the tunnel are constructed as tubes or boxes in a dry dock and fitted with temporary sealing ends. When the dry dock is flooded these sections either float immediately or are provided with additional bouyancy to do so, and are towed along the canal into position. They are sunk on to prepared level beds, and drawn tightly into position with the preceding sections. The temporary sealing ends at the junction are removed after the joint has been completed. The soil is then consolidated around them. This approach has been used on underwater tunnel crossings, for underground railways and roads and for large pipelines. On a different scale underwater pipelines can be constructed at ground level on soft land and towed, suspended by floats, along a flooded trench into position and sunk.

Another approach to the construction of box-like structures within saturated and soft soils is to use

caissons. Here the perimeter walls of the structure are constructed above water table level and encouraged to sink under their self-weight (or with added kentledge) as soil is removed from beneath them. Excavation may be carried out by the use of crane-operated grabs, by dredging methods, or by hand if a compressed air chamber is incorporated at the cutting toe level of the caisson unit. The proportion of the structure to be incorporated into the caisson depends on the design and depth of the permanent works, the nature of the soft saturated soils and on the method of excavation. It may be necessary to provide a temporary working platform at ground level on which to construct part of the perimeter wall. The ground can support this and then as the caisson is excavated in stages it can be extended vertically.

In very soft soils care should be taken that the caisson unit does not sink out of control. It is wise to investigate the soil at quarter points around the perimeter to be sure that uniform strata will be met and that a hard layer on one side does not divert the caisson in any way. Caissons exemplify the advantage of combining the design of the permanent works and the construction method to minimize the problems and extra costs of construction and temporary works.

12. OTHER METHODS USED TO COMBAT GROUNDWATER

Groundwater may also be controlled by preventing its movement and effects around the excavation or around and under a dam. This can be achieved by the use of grouted curtain walls or ground freezing.

Grouted curtain walls

The provision of an impermeable barrier or curtain around an excavation is made only when it is needed for a period of years rather than months and can be incorporated as a permanent improvement to the site. It will usually, but not necessarily, be installed some distance outside the face of the excavation and from the water table level down to an impermeable stratum. For shallow depths it may be economic to dig a trench and backfill it with compacted clay. For greater depths a membrane is formed by one of three methods.

The first is to auger to the required cut-off depth and mix cement and bentonite with the column of soil as the auger is withdrawn. A subsequent insertion of the auger overlaps with the previous one to provide continuity. In the second method, flat sheet steel piles are driven to the required cut-off depth and the annulus is filled with grout as the piles are withdrawn. Just sufficient piles are used in each location to separate the insertion and extraction operations. In the third method a comparatively narrow trench (600 mm) is excavated using the diaphragm wall technique and filled with a bentonite concrete to provide a continuous slurry concrete wall.

The installation of grout curtains is a conventional feature of dam construction to avoid water seepage through the ground on either side of and under the new construction. Many earth-fill dams are having slurry concrete cores constructed through them to counter increased permeability which has developed since they were constructed. As instanced by the grout curtains to dams, these cut-offs to groundwater are not always used as complete encirclements. Grout curtains are sometimes used to divert groundwater from flowing into and destabilizing permanent slopes and cliffs when quarries and other excavations are dug into hillsides.

Ground freezing

Groundwater freezing is an extreme method occasionally used before excavating to prevent large quantities of water moving into excavations. In fine soils where inflows of water canot be sealed off by the other conventional methods, pipes are drilled and inserted for the circulation of refrigerated brine solutions to freeze the water in the ground. Alternatively when ground freezing is required urgently for a short period, instead of using a recirculated refrigerant, liquid nitrogen can be injected directly into the area to be frozen. A sufficient depth of penetration is needed to ensure the integrity of the frozen soil to resist the pressures applied to it when excavation is undertaken. Ground freezing systems are effective, but expensive to install and operate. However, the operation costs are reduced when equilibrium is attained. In extremes, islands of frozen silts have been formed to support drilling equipment to carry out subsequent construction. There are also rare instances of ground being permanently frozen for the storage of cryogenic natural gas in unlined holes or for the support of structures.

REFERENCES

1. Somerville S. H. Construction Industry Research and Information Association, Report 113. *Practical control of groundwater on site*. CIRIA, London, 1986.
2. British Standards Institution. *Site investigation*. BSI, London, 1981, CP 5930.
3. Beaman A. L. and Jones R. D. Construction Industry Research and Information Association. Report 64. *Noise from construction and demolition sites*. CIRIA, London, 1977.
4. Terzaghi T. and Peck R. B. *Soil mechanics in engineering practice*. Wiley, Chichester, 1967.
5. Irvine D. J. and Smith R. J. H. Construction Industry Research and Information Association. Technical Report 97. *Trenching practice*. CIRIA, London, 1983.
6. Mackay E. B. Construction Industry Research and Information Association. Technical Note 95 *Proprietary trench support systems*. CIRIA, London, 1979.
7. Greenwood D. A. and Thomson G. H. *Ground*

stabilisation — deep compaction & grouting. ICE Works Construction Guide. Thomas Telford Ltd, London, 1984.
8. Muir Wood A. M. *Civil Engineers' Reference Book.* ch.30, *Newnes-Butterworth, London, 1975.*
9. British Standards Institution. *Earthworks.* BSI, London, 1981, CP 6031.
10. Transport and Road Research Laboratory. *A guide to the structural design of pavements for new roads.* Department of Transport technical memorandum H6/78.TRRL, Crowthorne, 1970, Road note 29.

BIBLIOGRAPHY

British Standards Institution. *Noise control on construction and demolition sites.* BSI, London, 1975, CP 5228.
Construction (General Provisions) Regulations. Building Employers Confederation, London, 1961.
Tomlinson M. J. *Foundation design and construction,* 5th edn. Longmans, Harlow, 1986.

ICE WORKS CONSTRUCTION GUIDES

Other guides in the series

Available from: Thomas Telford Ltd, Marketing and Sales Department
1–7 Great George Street, London SW1P 3AA
Telephone: 01–222 7722

Thomas Telford

Learning Resources
Centre